Bayonne Bridge

A Landmark by Land, Sea, and Air

This book is dedicated on the 75th anniversary of the Bayonne Bridge to all the proud and skillful builders who helped create this beautiful structure; to the men and women of the Port Authority who operated and maintained the bridge for the first 75 years; and to their colleagues who lost their lives at The World Trade Center on February 26, 1993, and on September 11, 2001.

Bayonne Bridge
A Landmark by Land, Sea, and Air

By Darl Rastorfer

The Port Authority of New York and New Jersey
www.panynj.info

Designed by Andrea Hemmann/GHI Design, Philadelphia, PA
Printed in Canada by Transcontinental Litho Acme, Montréal

ISBN-13: 978-0-9789640-1-6
ISBN-10: 0-9789640-1-2

Published by The Port Authority of
New York and New Jersey
in association with
Darl Rastorfer and Associates.

Bayonne Bridge
A Landmark by Land, Sea, and Air

DARL RASTORFER

The Bayonne Bridge is among The Port Authority of New York and New Jersey's oldest facilities. The bistate agency was created in 1921 to promote and protect the commerce of the New York and New Jersey metropolitan area. In just ten years, the Port Authority built and opened four bridges: the Goethals Bridge and the Outerbridge Crossing (both 1928), and the George Washington and Bayonne bridges (both 1931); issued the first version of the consolidated revenue bond to establish a funding source for building new regional transportation infrastructure; and assumed responsibility for the Holland Tunnel.

When making plans for the Bayonne Bridge, the Port Authority asked the designer for a structure that would be both functional and beautiful. The bridge, designed by Othmar H. Ammann, is both. It opened to the traveling public on November 15, 1931, and quickly became a welcoming presence throughout the region.

Through the years, the Port Authority further expanded the region's interconnected roadways, harbors, and airports. The Bayonne Bridge, with its commanding position at the top of the Kill Van Kull, provided a dazzling visual point of reference for much of that development. The bridge is a cherished landmark for the millions who travel through the region and for the communities it serves. This book celebrates the Bayonne Bridge on its 75th anniversary.

ANTHONY R. COSCIA, *Chairman*
CHARLES A. GARGANO, *Vice Chairman*
KENNETH J. RINGLER JR., *Executive Director*
The Port Authority of New York and New Jersey
November 15, 2006

Contents

Drawing of a proposed decorative stone wall designed to rest on the abutment of the bridge's arch. The designer of the bridge, Othmar H. Ammann, and his consulting architect, Cass Gilbert, proposed the ornamental stonework, illustrated in this drawing, as a graceful transition between the massive concrete piers of the viaduct and the open steelwork of the arch. Ultimately, due to financial considerations, the open steelwork was chosen over the ornamental design.

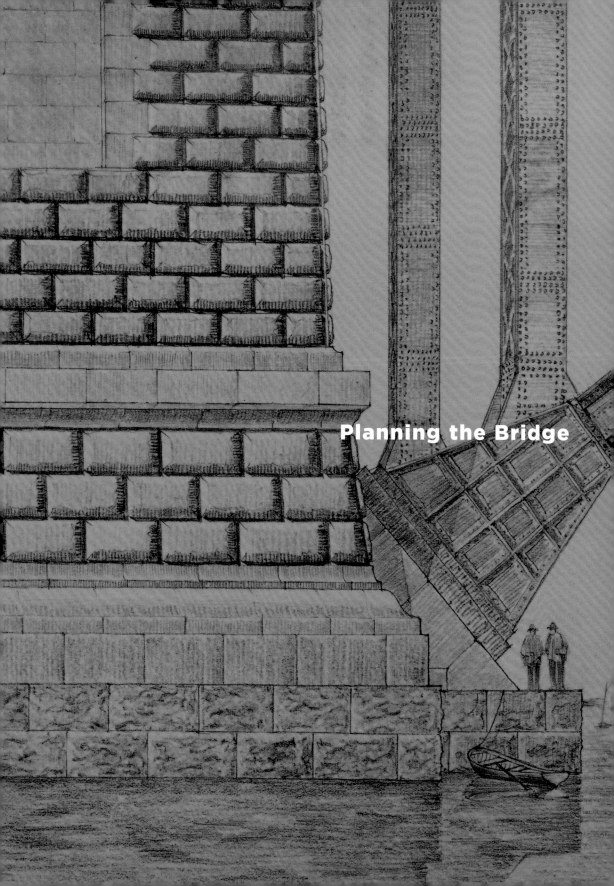

Planning the Bridge

The Bayonne Bridge crosses the Kill Van Kull to connect the roadways of Bayonne, New Jersey with those of Port Richmond, New York. It is one of three bridges that was built between New Jersey and Staten Island by The Port Authority of New York and New Jersey from 1926 to 1931. All three — the Bayonne, Goethals, and Outerbridge Crossing — were constructed with the expectation that New York City would simultaneously complete a tunnel or bridge on the eastern side of Staten Island, which would connect to Brooklyn. When the Verrazano-Narrows Bridge opened in 1964, traffic volume spiked on the Port Authority's three bridges between New Jersey and Staten Island.

These sketches (opposite) for a suspension bridge over the Kill Van Kull are among the first design studies made for the crossing. A suspension bridge for the site was appropriate for motor vehicles. When the commissioners of the Port Authority decided that the span should accommodate rail traffic too, the designers abandoned a conventional suspension structure in favor of an arch with a record-breaking span.

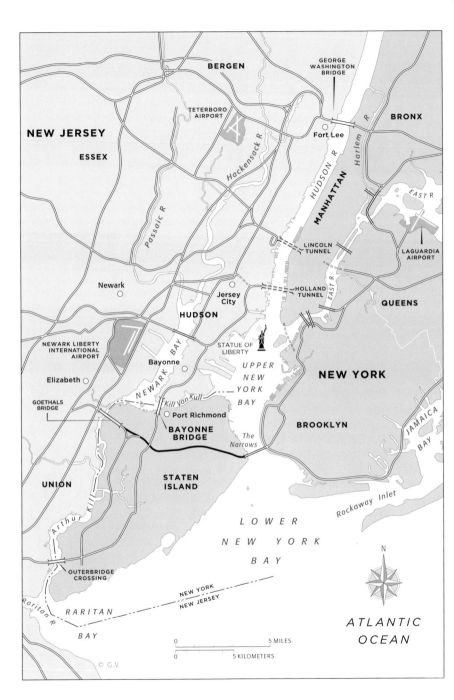

THE BAYONNE BRIDGE WAS THE LAST OF THREE RELATED BRIDGES planned by The Port Authority of New York and New Jersey (then the Port of New York Authority) to connect New Jersey with Staten Island. They were built as part of a circumferential highway network envisioned for the greater New York metropolitan region. In addition to its role in the regional network, planners speculated that the Bayonne Bridge would serve automobile traffic from commuters who worked in Lower Manhattan and lived in bedroom communities on Staten Island — communities that would spring up as a result of the bridge.

The site selected for the bridge paralleled an existing ferry service between Bayonne and Port Richmond. By building over the ferry route, the planners preserved the street patterns of both towns. However, this arrangement also meant that the bridge would cross the Kill Van Kull slightly askew, requiring a longer span than a right-angle crossing.

Initially, the bridge was planned for motor vehicles, bicycles, and pedestrians only. Accordingly, a suspension bridge design was developed since this type of bridge offered the most economical way to engineer a single span across the Kill Van Kull for motor vehicles. However, the suspension scheme was abandoned when the Port Authority commissioners insisted that considerations be made for at least two rail transit tracks — to be added at some future date. (Studies showed that adapting a suspension design for rail traffic would be cost-prohibitive.) With rail traffic in mind, the bridge's chief designer, Othmar H. Ammann, began developing a scheme that spanned the Kill Van Kull with a single, innovative, arch-shaped truss. As with the suspension bridge scheme, Ammann worked on the arch design in partnership with architect Cass Gilbert. The arch bridge that emerged promised to be a remarkably efficient solution that was well suited to the site from both an engineering and aesthetic standpoint.

Because the arch spans a shipping channel, the suspended roadway would be held 150 feet above water level — clearance for the U.S. Navy's tallest ships in the 1930s. To get the roadway from ground level to 150 feet in the air, a viaduct would be built on both ends of the arch. Monumental in their own right, the viaducts and the arch would support one and a quarter miles of elevated roadways.

The American Institute of Steel Construction selected the Bayonne Bridge as the most beautiful steel bridge, costing over $1 million, to open to traffic in 1931. As Ammann stated at the opening ceremony, "The Port Authority recognized the fact that its structures must not only be useful, but they must also conform to the aesthetic sense. This was one of the motives for the selection of an arch spanning the entire river in one sweeping graceful curve."

Construction of the great steel arch began in Port Richmond. Construction of the base of the arch on the New Jersey side has not yet begun.

Construction

12 The long approach roads to the bridge's central span are carried by a series of reinforced concrete piers. The legs of the piers are connected at their tops with reinforced concrete arches. The shortest piers are 20 feet tall. The tallest piers stand 110 feet — as tall as a ten-story building. The roadway carried by the Port Richmond viaduct is approximately 2,010 feet long and the Bayonne viaduct is approximately 3,010 feet long. In all, with approaches, the structure is approximately one and two-thirds miles.

The Bayonne Bridge's arch had to be assembled without blocking the Kill Van Kull's shipping channel. To meet the challenge, engineers devised a temporary support system that used hydraulic jacks. Sections of the truss cantilevered over the support system as the arch grew toward its connecting point.

Hoisting and connecting pre-assembled sections of the road deck to pre-cut steel cable rope, hung from the arch.

CONSTRUCTION OF THE BAYONNE BRIDGE began in September 1928. The projected date of completion was early 1932. Thanks to thoughtful planning, careful management, and ingenious construction technology, the $13-million bridge was completed in November 1931 — several months ahead of schedule, and $3 million under budget.

Constructing the arch posed a special challenge. Most arches are built using a fully formed, temporary support system that mirrors the curve of the completed arch. However, such a system could not be used for the Bayonne Bridge since it would block shipping on the Kill Van Kull, one of the world's busiest channels. In response, a method was devised to build the Bayonne Bridge's arch using truss segments, which were fabricated off-site, transported to the bridge, lifted into position, and attached to the previously assembled segment. Moveable hydraulic jacks were used to prop up the arch during erection.

Once constructed, the truss was the world's longest. To this day the truss stands as one of the world's most elegant arches, made of a sleek and modulated form of high-strength alloy steel.

Workers tighten bolts that secure a reinforcing plate where steel ropes thread through to support a suspended beam of the road deck.

The Bayonne Bridge was dedicated during a ribbon cutting ceremony the day before it opened to the public. On opening day, November 15, 1931, at 5 a.m., over 17,000 vehicles and nearly 7,000 pedestrians crossed the bridge. The American Institute of Steel Construction selected the Bayonne Bridge as the most beautiful steel bridge, costing more than $1 million, to open to traffic in 1931.

The Bridge Opens to the Public

A pedestrian on the walkway in the 1930s looks toward the bridge's roadway.

FOR 45 YEARS, THE BAYONNE BRIDGE was the world's longest steel-arch bridge. At 1,675 feet, the arch is 70 percent longer than the previous record holder, the Hell Gate Railroad Bridge in New York City. When the Port Authority opened the Bayonne Bridge in 1931, its "sister bridge," the Sydney Harbour Bridge, was under construction in Australia. It closely follows the design of the Bayonne Bridge, but its span is 25 inches shorter, and it wasn't until 1977 that the New River Gorge Bridge in West Virginia surpassed the Bayonne Bridge in length with an arch of 1,700 feet.

At the Bayonne Bridge dedication ceremony on November 14, 1931, representatives from the Sydney Harbour Bridge Commission participated in the ribbon-cutting ceremony where a pair of custom-made golden scissors were used at the event. Four months later, a delegation from New York and New Jersey participated in the ribbon cutting for the Sydney Harbour Bridge. The same scissors were used, and following the ceremony, the scissors were taken apart and each bridge authority carried away a golden blade.

In 1951, the Port Authority and the City of Bayonne redesigned the bridge's New Jersey toll plaza with new shrubbery, trees, benches, and walks. In 1956, a portion of the land under the Bayonne Bridge approach was made available by the Port Authority to the Bayonne community for the Juliette Street Playground. A new toll plaza on the Staten Island side, with an administrative office building, was completed in 1964. In 1970, one-way toll collection was implemented at the Port Richmond Plaza.

The bridge is an ever-present and deeply appreciated part of the Bayonne community, and many residents have cherished memories of it. One is Norman B. Resnick, whose recollections were published in the *Bayonne Community News* on the occasion of the bridge's 50th anniversary in 1981. Mr. Resnick recalls walking across the bridge on the day it opened, which also was his eighth birthday. "I was only interested in looking at the high arch and down to the clean waters of the Kill Van Kull." Prior to the bridge's opening, Resnick recalled his family traveling to Staten Island via the Bayonne-Richmond Ferry. On Staten Island, they drove through farmlands, gathered wild mushrooms, and visited pristine beaches. Mr. Resnick's tribute to the bridge concluded with, "The feature of the city that I brag about most to outsiders is the Bayonne Bridge, the longest steel-arch span in the world."

Crossing under the arch from a motorist's perspective.

The Bayonne Bridge as seen from the air in the 1940s: Port Richmond is in the foreground; Newark Bay is at the upper left; the skyline of Manhattan can be seen on the horizon at the right.

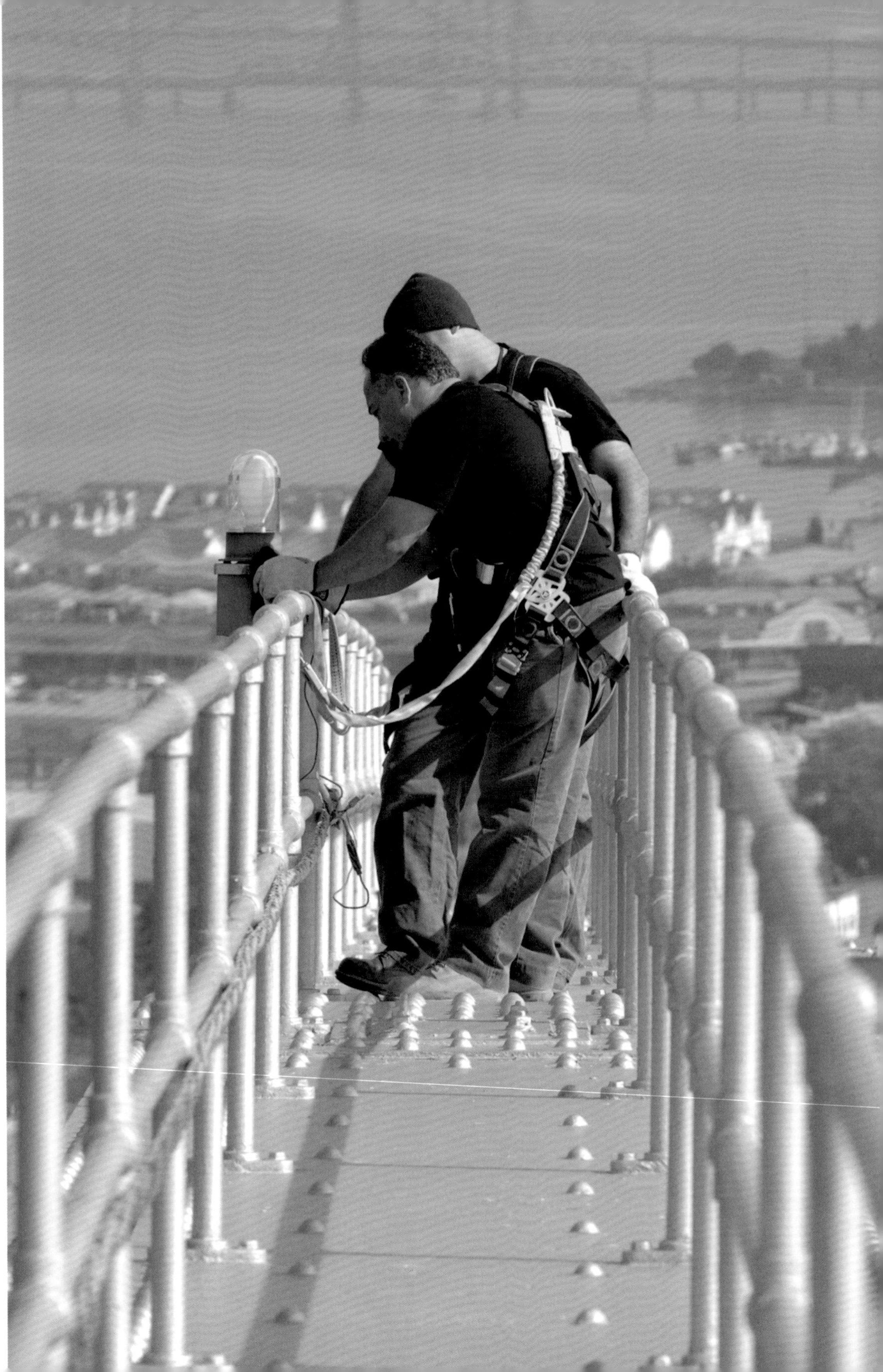

The Bayonne Bridge at night (above). On September 11, 2002, in honor of the victims of the September 11, 2001 attacks on The World Trade Center, the Bayonne Bridge's arch lighting was colored red, white, and blue with red lights on the Port Richmond side, blue lights on the Bayonne side, and white at the middle third. Now a permanent feature, the idea was suggested by Veronica Marie Granite, an eight-year-old Bayonne resident.

Bridge electricians relamp the arch (opposite and above). Electricians in harnesses tied to the bridge, walk along the top of the arch and replace burnt out lamps with new ones.

Port Richmond in the foreground; in the upper left corner, the Kill Van Kull merges with Newark Bay.

A Landmark by Land, Sea, and Air

The Bayonne Bridge is an integral part of Bayonne's identity and streetscape. Views of the bridge pop up throughout the community. This photograph was taken at Third Street looking down John F. Kennedy Boulevard.

THE BAYONNE BRIDGE'S SWEEPING ARCH soars above the low-lying landscapes and waterways of the region, making it a cherished landmark for millions of people who travel through the region by land, sea, and air.

The bridge has special landmark status in the two communities it joins: Bayonne, New Jersey and Port Richmond, Staten Island. Bayonne residents, in particular, embrace the bridge that rises out of their community while providing a backdrop to a municipal park on the water, the Mayor Dennis P. Collins Park.

Filming *War of the Worlds*
(top). Hollywood came to
Bayonne in November 2004
to record the opening scenes
of a movie adaptation of the
H.G. Wells classic. Directed
by Steven Spielberg, the
story opens as its lead
character, Bayonne resident
Ray Ferrier (played by actor
Tom Cruise) leaves his job on
the docks for his Bayonne
home on John F. Kennedy
Boulevard, two blocks from
the bridge. In the background
of this behind-the-scenes
glimpse of a filming session
you can see a concrete pier
that supports one of the
bridge's viaducts.

As part of an official
celebration on the occasion
of the 75th anniversary of
the Bayonne Bridge
(middle), 75 red, white, and
blue tulips were planted in
Mayor Dennis P. Collins Park
in Bayonne by New Jersey
Governor Jon S. Corzine
(foreground), Bayonne
Mayor Joseph V. Doria, Jr.
(not pictured), and students
from Bayonne and Staten
Island public schools.

Playground in Bayonne's
Mayor Dennis P. Collins Park
(bottom). Situated between
West 1st Street, the Kill
Van Kull shoreline, and the
bridge, the park has walking
trails, baseball and softball
fields, basketball courts,
tennis courts, a wading
pool, a dock, and seating
throughout.

House fronts along John F. Kennedy Boulevard in Bayonne. All of these houses have backyards with direct views of the bridge.

Aerial view of the Bayonne Bridge above the Kill Van Kull. The Kill Van Kull is one of the world's busiest shipping channels, connecting the ports of Newark and Upper New York bays with other ports around the world.

The crane in the foreground is on a New Jersey dock and is used to unload cargo from container ships (opposite). The arch truss of the Bayonne Bridge gleams in the background in this photograph taken from a boat as it leaves Port Newark.

Deepening the Kill Van Kull federal channel to 50 feet (below). As part of a federal channel deepening project sponsored by the Port Authority and managed by the U.S. Army Corps of Engineers, the contractor is using its backhoe dredge, the MARICAVOR, to remove blasted rock and hard material from the channel bottom.

32 Acknowledgments

This book was produced thanks to the support of a number of talented, knowledgeable, and dedicated people at The Port Authority of New York and New Jersey.

I gained invaluable insight into the planning, operation, maintenance, and history of the bridge through a series of interviews with Port Authority personnel. Interviewees included: Anthony R. Coscia, Chairman; Charles A. Gargano, Vice Chairman; Kenneth J. Ringler Jr., Executive Director; Ernesto L. Butcher, Chief Operating Officer; Francis J. Lombardi, Chief Engineer; Gerard DelTufo, General Manager, Bayonne and Goethals bridges and Outerbridge Crossing.

Many thanks to Rae Ann Hoffmann and Audrey Mancher, who provided direction and guidance in the creative process. Thanks especially to Connie Nardella who coordinated every detail of the book's development, including archival and photographic research.

My sincere appreciation to Kayla M. Bergeron, Chief, Public and Government Affairs; Victoria Cross Kelly, Director, Tunnels, Bridges and Terminals; John J. McCarthy, Director, Public Affairs; Stephen R. Napolitano, Assistant Director, Operations, Tunnels, Bridges and Terminals; and Kevin J. Kirchman, Deputy Director, Public Affairs, for their enthusiastic support of this project.

Thanks also to Herbert S. Somerwitz, Chief, Contracts Division, Law Department, for his legal guidance, and to the following staff members who provided administrative support, research, review, insight, and photographs: Cynthia Armour, Terry Benczik, Bill Cahill, Michael Dombrowski, Frank Gallo, Tina Hansen, Russell Jordan, Rudolph L. King, Jr., Robin D. Lance, Joyce Martinsen, Frank Radics, and Tiffany Townsend. Other assistance was provided by Richard Lewis and F. Patrick Carolan of Korey Kay & Partners. Projects in the Design Arts, Inc. provided photographic prints.

Finally, my gratitude to a number of people in Bayonne, New Jersey and Staten Island, New York, who provided history, guidance, documents, and photographs: Dr. Joseph E. Ryan, Public Information Director, City of Bayonne; Augie Caamano, Jr., Bayonne Webmaster; Lee Fahley, President, Bayonne Historical Society; P. Gerard Nowicki, Trustee, Bayonne Historical Society; John Guild, Executive Director, and Carlotta DeFillo, Librarian, Staten Island Historical Society; and Al Sullivan, Hudson Reporter Associates.

DARL RASTORFER